MW00637843

The Power of Genetics: DNA, daily decisions, and the journey to taking control of your health
Copyright © 2022, 3X4 Genetics
Foreword: Dr. Sara Gottfried MD
Design and illustration: Carmen van Vuuren, Drew Dovey, Nicole Hagan and Robyn Mitchell
Editor: Klara Mudge
Printed in the USA.

www.3X4genetics.com

All rights reserved. No part of this publication may be reproduced or distributed in any form or by any means, electronic or mechanical, including but not limited to digital copying and printing, or be stored in a database or retrieval system, without prior written permission from the author.

The Power of Genetics is intended solely for informational and educational purposes and not as personal medical advice. Always seek the advice of your healthcare provider with any questions you have regarding a medical condition, and before undertaking any diet, exercise, or other health program.

The information in this book is not intended to treat, diagnose, cure, or prevent any disease. The author and 3X4 Genetics accepts no liability of any kind for any damages caused or alleged to be caused, directly or indirectly, from use of the information in this book.

The Power of Genetics

DNA, daily decisions, and the journey to taking control of your health

by **Dr. Yael Joffe, PhD**

Crucial Truths Are Locked in Your Genes.

When unlocked, they can completely change the way you think about your body.

The assumption for so long has been that we are our genes and therefore trapped by the past. Before scientists sequenced the entire human genome in 2003, people figured DNA was the final blueprint for health and disease, forever fixed. If your mother had Alzheimer's disease and your father had a premature heart attack, you would probably suffer the same fate. Treatment for chronic disease was one-size-fits-all. Diabetic? Try this pill. Depressed?

Here is a prescription for a selective serotonin reuptake inhibitor. Did this approach work for chronic disease? Not so much.

What a breakthrough to discover the full genetic code, and further, that genetic expression is malleable! I expected that medicine would be immediately transformed. Unfortunately, the healthcare revolution kept getting postponed. Meanwhile, in conventional medicine, we persisted in the practice of imprecision medicine. We learned that for certain antidepressants about nine patients need to be treated

for one to benefit. The statistics are even more grim when it comes to statin therapy: approximately 20 to 50 need to be treated for one to benefit. These approaches fail to understand the gene / environment conversation and therefore do not address the root cause.

Imagine a different type of healthcare where we know all about you as an individual. We know with precision the specific types of nutrition and lifestyle tweaks that might help work around your genetics. We address problems like a rising fasting glucose with targeted dietary and exercise change before pills. We address the root cause rather than masking symptoms. If you need a medication, we can choose one with greater insight.

It took longer than expected, but now it's happening. The revolution is here. This accessible consumer-friendly book you are holding is evidence of how far we've come.

We're in the era of biological design, learning more and more about the role of genetics, including the way our DNA interacts with lifestyle and environment in ways that are complex and thrilling. In the work that I do in precision medicine, where I'm working with a team and integrating multiple data streams to understand in a comprehensive way the patient in front of us, genetics is an essential part of the process. We are finally moving from medicine for the average person to medicine for the individual, and genetics plays a foundational role in phenotype, the observable characteristics of a person resulting from the dialogue between genes and environment. Deep knowledge of your phenotype allows us to personalize care. One of our key tools in precision medicine is performing experiments that focus on a single person where they serve as their own control. This is called the N-of-1 trial – and this allows us to determine if you will benefit from an intervention. Once again, I find that awareness of genetic blueprint is critical to successful N-of-1 experiments and improved health.

This book is the good news we need now.

You are not a slave to your genes. You have the power to reconfigure the way your DNA talks to your body. You can improve the environment for your genes with your daily choices for body and mind, both conscious and unconscious, including what you eat and drink, how often you move and what form that movement takes, what environmental exposures you have in your home and work, and how you manage (or not) your stress.

Where do you begin this empowered journey? Start here, with the basic truths inside this book.

- SARA GOTTFRIED MD,
Four-time *New York Times* Best-selling Author
Berkeley, California

4

CONTENTS

FOREWORD

3 Crucial Truths Are Locked in Your Genes

INTRODUCTION

7 You, your body, and your health journey are all entirely unique to you

PART 1

GENETICS 101

11 What Are Genes?

13 What Is Genetics?

14 A Brief History of Genetics

15 How Do Genes Work?

16 Why Is It Important to Understand Your Genes?

17 What People Get Wrong About Genes

19 Top 10 Genetics Terms

PART 2

WHY GENES MAKE US DIFFERENT

23 DNA Is the Language of Inheritance

24 Genetic Variation

25 SNPs

26 Not All SNPs Carry Equal Consequence

27 How Do We Switch Genes On and Off?

28 How Vicky Discovered the Root Cause of Her Migraines

PART 3

HOW GENETICS IMPACTS OUR LIVES

31   Moving From Symptoms to Source

33   H=G+C Brings It All Together

35   Arina Finally Found Her Healthy Weight

36   Why Do We Group Genes Together?

37   What Insights Can the Pathways Give Us?

39   The Story of Broccoli

40   What Is a DNA Diet?

41   Five Myths About Dieting and Your Genes

43   Can Your DNA Give You Dieting Advice?

44   Genetics and Eating

44   Genetics and Coffee

44   Genetics and Inflammation

45   The Story of Fatima

PART 4

THE STORY OF YOUR GENES

49   Extra! Extra! Read All About You

PART 5

UNDERSTANDING YOUR GENES

53   How Can You Understand Your Genes?

54   What Is Genetic Testing and How Does it Work?

55   Najwa's Genetics Story

56   What Are the Different Types of Genetics Tests?

56   How Do You Choose the Right Test for You?

57   10 Reasons to Test your Genes

59   Your Health Journey

61   The Story of Gordon

PART 6

TAKING CONTROL OF YOUR HEALTH

65   From DNA Data to Daily Decisions

CONCLUSION

You, your body, and your health journey are all entirely unique to you.

If you don't understand your body, and the unique ways in which it works, how will you understand what choices to make for it?

Most approaches to health and wellness today prescribe one-size-fits-all solutions to human beings — human beings who are vastly different in so many ways. From height to energy levels to how much sleep we need at night, each one of us is unique.

Isn't it about time healthcare recognizes our uniqueness and finds better ways to give individuals solutions as unique as they are?

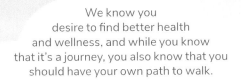

We know you
desire to find better health
and wellness, and while you know
that it's a journey, you also know that you
should have your own path to walk.

The blueprint for building that
longer, healthier, and richer life can
be found in your genes. The most
effective and science-backed way to provide
that kind of personalization is through
the power of genetics.

Now is the time to
take the next step towards
more personalized healthcare that
will not only be tailored to your unique make-up,
but will also optimize how your body functions,
and help you make choices that could lead to a
longer, healthier, and richer life.

Let's get started on the journey!

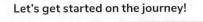

PART 1
GENETICS
101

What Are Genes?

So much of who we are as individuals is determined by our genes.

Some people are natural runners, some have artistic talent.

Our genetic variations can affect how we metabolize our food, how we break down toxins, how we make energy in our cells, and so much more!

Some people are tall, and some are shorter.

Some people can have caffeine in the evening, while others are more sensitive to caffeine's sleep-disrupting effects.

Some people have blue eyes, and some have brown.

Genes are passed from parents to children and form part of our chromosomes. They're what make us unique because they carry the information that creates our unique traits.

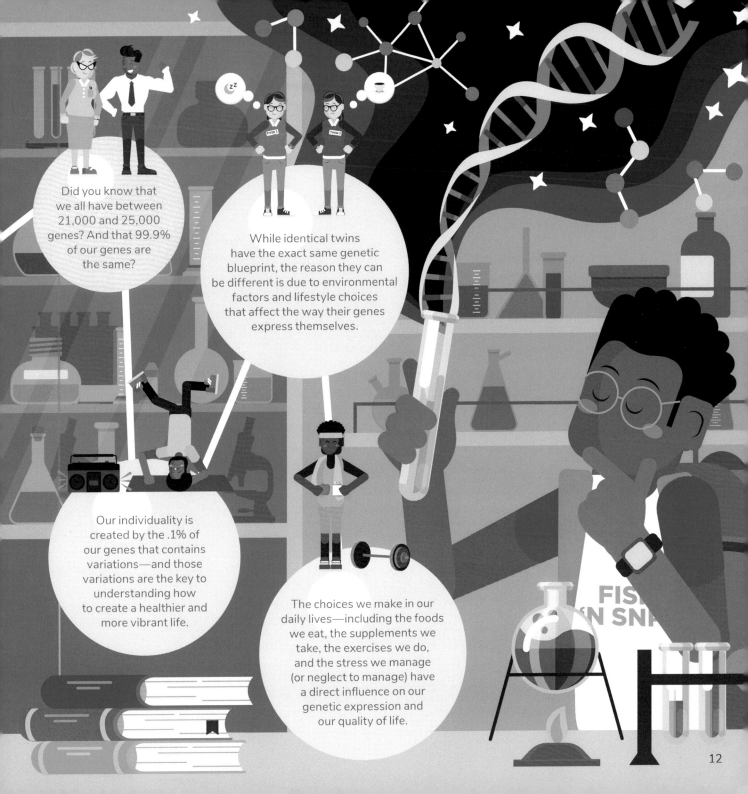

Did you know that we all have between 21,000 and 25,000 genes? And that 99.9% of our genes are the same?

While identical twins have the exact same genetic blueprint, the reason they can be different is due to environmental factors and lifestyle choices that affect the way their genes express themselves.

Our individuality is created by the .1% of our genes that contains variations—and those variations are the key to understanding how to create a healthier and more vibrant life.

The choices we make in our daily lives—including the foods we eat, the supplements we take, the exercises we do, and the stress we manage (or neglect to manage) have a direct influence on our genetic expression and our quality of life.

12

What Is Genetics?

Genetics is the study of genes and their effects on our bodies, how traits are passed down through families, and the specific information that each gene contains. More importantly, it's the study of variations that impact how our bodies respond to the world around us, and how the lifestyle choices we make impact how our genes express themselves. It's what gives us a blueprint we can use to build a healthier, longer life.

1900s
Mendel's theories gain traction and credibility

1866
Gregor Mendel derives a theory of genetics through his work around plant heredity

1950s
DNA studies begin

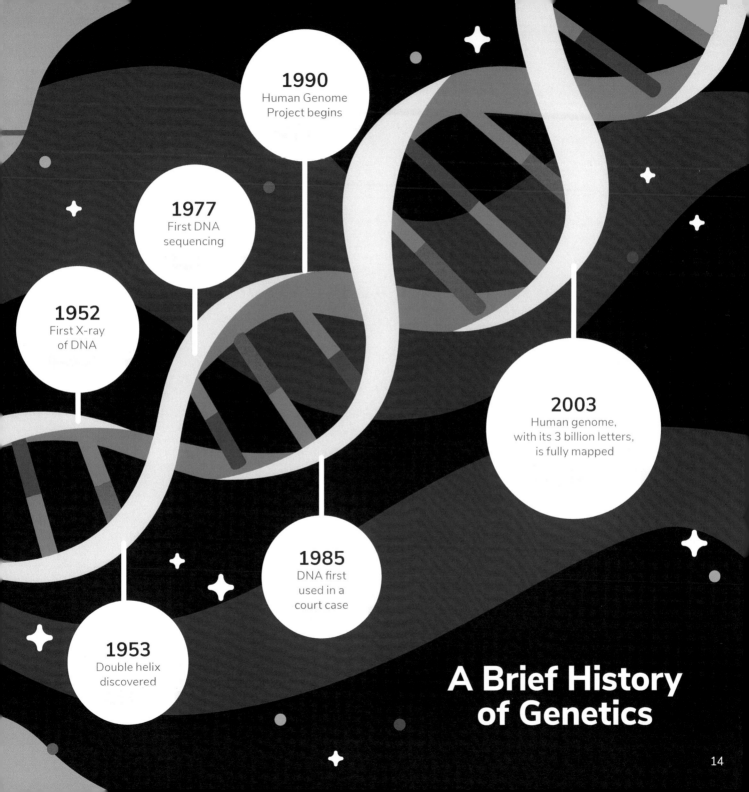

1952
First X-ray
of DNA

1977
First DNA
sequencing

1990
Human Genome
Project begins

2003
Human genome,
with its 3 billion letters,
is fully mapped

1953
Double helix
discovered

1985
DNA first
used in a
court case

A Brief History
of Genetics

How Do Genes Work?

Think of your genes like a set of blueprints, unique to you.

DNA IS THE FOUNDATION

DNA carries all the information needed to "build" a human being, made up of four bases or 'letters' (GACT).

G · A · C · T

INTO THE FUTURE

A personalized plan creates a path for health and wellness going forward.

BUILDING BLOCKS

These four letters of DNA, when put into groups of three, create the proteins that make up all the important elements in our body.

UNDERSTANDING IMPACT

Variations in the order of these letters can impact the structure and function of amino acids, proteins, enzymes, and hormones.

OUR UNIQUE .1%

Variations can occur in our DNA through substitution, deletion, insertion, and multiple copies of genes.

BLUEPRINT FOR HEALTH

Knowing each variation means we know how each individual body works at the cellular level—it's unique for each person.

INDIVIDUALIZED CARE

Each individual can follow their unique blueprint, based on their genetic make-up, to lead them towards optimal health.

Why Is It Important to Understand Your Genes?

Understanding your genes has its benefits. Here are a few.

Clarity

Understanding your genes provides clarity as to why your body responds the way it does to certain foods and environments, and how to help your body's systems work optimally.

Food Choices

Understanding your genes lets you sync up your body to the right foods for it, which can improve energy levels, digestion, detoxification, longevity, and many other functions.

Supplements

Understanding your genes can help to narrow down which supplements might have the biggest impact on your body's functionality and health, which can save you having to go through trial and error.

Focus

Understanding your genes gives you focus in the areas of your health and wellness that need improvement, as well as insight into potential underlying root causes of chronic symptoms.

Screening

Understanding your genes shines a light on areas that may need more testing and screening, which can help mitigate health risks and prevent chronic illness.

What People Get Wrong About Genes

Common myths and misconceptions around genetic testing.

$2^2 + 1\ \mathcal{E} = 0.005$

"Genetic results are set in stone."

While we can't change our DNA, we can certainly make lifestyle decisions that can impact how our genes express themselves for better or worse. We essentially can control our own destiny through the choices we make.

"Genetic insights are used in isolation, as the ultimate truth."

To understand and test your body, a comprehensive evaluation of family history, activity, diet, environment, and more is needed. Genetic insights are never used in isolation.

"The science isn't there yet to support genetic testing."

Like with all science, our knowledge of genes and how they impact our body's functionality is always evolving and growing—and we can use the evidence base we already have on nutrigenomics to start helping people personalize their health.

"Genetic testing is only used to predict disease."

While genetic testing can be used to predict disease, it can also be helpful in pointing the way to the source of chronic illness that can be improved or healed through different choices.

TCG
ACT
CTG
GAT
CAG
CTG
ACT
GAT
CTG
ACT
GAT

17

"Practitioners should only focus on one or two genes."

Just like you wouldn't take one or two instruments out of an orchestra, genes need to be understood in the context of how they interact with other genes to impact health and functionality.

"Genetic testing is all about ancestry and predicting disease."

Even though we often hear about genetic tests discovering ancestry or disease, genetic testing can help inform everyday lifestyle choices to create optimal health and wellness in all different ways.

"Genetic results are not private, and will be shared."

There are laws in place, like the Genetic Information Nondiscrimination Act (GINA), that prohibit testing companies from sharing information with third parties, your employer, or your insurance company.

Begun in 1990, the **Human Genome Project** was an international initiative that set out to map every gene in the human body, or the human genome. When it was completed in 2003, the Project found that we have about 20,500 genes. The Project also found out more about how genes function and are structured in our bodies. The information was made public so that scientists, practitioners, and everyone can further their knowledge of how the human body works.

18

Top 10 Genetics Terms

Brush up on your need-to-know vocabulary.

her·i·ta·bil·i·ty
(hĕr'ĭ-tə-bəl)

n. The measure of how differences in genes account for differences in various traits.

chro·mo·some
(krō'mə-sōm')

n. Chromosomes are located in the nucleus of cells and made up of coiled DNA and protein.

gene var·i·a·tion
(jēn vâr'ē-ā'shən, văr'-)

n. It's the variation in the .1% of genes that create unique traits and features.

DNA (dē'ĕn-ā')
(deoxyribonucleic acid)

n. Formed of four chemical bases in different combinations, DNA is what makes up the basics of our chromosomes. DNA is hereditary and found in nearly every organism.

ge·nome
(jē'nōm')

n. A collection of someone's complete set of genes that provides all the information about their genetic makeup.

ge·net·ic mark·er

n. A genetic marker is where a specific DNA sequence is found on a chromosome.

gene ther·a·py
(jēn thĕr'ə-pē)

n. Administering or replacing faulty genes with healthy genetic material to help treat disease.

ge·net·ic dis·eases
(jə-nĕt'ĭk dĭ-zēz')

n. A disease caused by altered or variant genes.

ge·net·ic test·ing

n. A genetic test identifies genes and genetic variations through blood or saliva analysis.

CRISPR
(clusters of regularly interspaced short palindromic repeats)

CRISPR is a method of gene editing.

PART 2
WHY GENES
MAKE US
DIFFERENT

DNA Is the Language of Inheritance

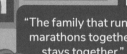
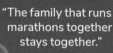

"You have the same eyes as your mother!"

"Wow, everyone in your family is tall, aren't they?"

"The family that runs marathons together stays together."

But if we are 99.9% identical, what happens with the 0.1%?

We call DNA "the language of inheritance" because it's what passes traits from parents to children throughout the generations. If you ever look through old family photos, you may notice that. In fact, our DNA is 99.9% the same.

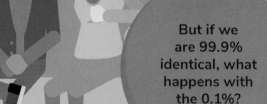
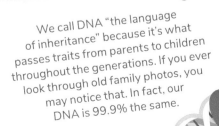

Genetic Variation

.1%

IN OUT
A → G

Despite being just .1%, genetic variation is what makes us unique, from physical aspects like hair and eye color, height, and metabolism, to how our bodies react to caffeine, sleep, and different types of exercise and environments. That .1% may be small, but it's valuable! Change happens in our DNA through substitution, deletion, insertion, and copied numbers.

Substitution

T A C   C T G   C A G
↓
T G C   C T G   C A G

Deletion

T A C   C T G   C A G
↓
T A C   C G   C A G
↘ T

Insertion

T A C   C T G   C A G
↓
T A C   C C T G   C A G

QUEUE HERE

Copied numbers

T A C   C T G   C A G
↓
T C A   C T G   C A G

TAC TAC
TCA TCA
TCA TCA

These types of variations are not only what make us unique — they create the individualized blueprint that gives us insight into how our individual bodies function at a cellular level.

SNPs

To get more specific, the variations on the previous page are called SNPs (pronounced 'snips'). A SNP, or a single nucleotide polymorphism, is a typical genetic variation in a person's DNA. There are more than 100 million different SNPs that have been discovered, and a person may have 4 to 5 million SNPs in their own genome! When we look at variations that make people unique, we're looking for different SNPs. And those SNPs carry the key to personalization.

Dr. Yael's Top 8 Snps

 APOE
"The God Gene": inflammation for survival

 ACE
"The Hooligan": fitness, endurance or power

 GSTM1
"Garbage Removal": getting rid of toxins

 TNFA
"Fire-Breather": switching on inflammation

 MTHFR
"Relay Race": keeps methylation moving!

 HFE
"Silent Killer": iron storage vault

 COMT
"Swiss Army Knife": it does a bit of everything!

 NQ01
"The Gatekeeper": protects against DNA damage

Not All SNPs Carry Equal Consequence

Not all SNPs are the same! Some SNPs are high penetrance while others are low. Another word for penetrance would be impact.

High Penetrance

These genetic variations are powerful and have a high chance of impacting someone's health, more so than lifestyle choice or environment. Think of them as the loud ones at the party!

Low Penetrance

These genetic variations are less likely to have a high impact on someone's health by themselves, but they interact with diet and lifestyle choices. Think of them as the wallflowers at the party! This is the world of nutrigenomics.

MUTATION OR VARIATION?

When the field of genetics was developing, the term "mutation" was used to describe a variation, but one that tended to have a high penetrance and would more likely cause disease. However, we want to evaluate all high- and low-penetrance SNPs, and feel that the term "mutation" is alarmist for many, so we use the more neutral term: variations.

How Do We Switch Genes On and Off?

"But my genes are set in stone — I can't change them!"

We hear this often, don't we? While an individual can't change their DNA, the way their genes express themselves—or switch on or off—can be influenced by many different factors, like diet, mood, seasons, medication, and more.

This is called "epigenetics," which means "above the genes." Rather than believe that our genetics lock us in to a specific health destiny, we "go above the genes" to look at the ways environment and lifestyle choices can influence how our different genes express themselves—giving us a clear path to better health.

FISH 'N SNPs

SOUP

"Your genetics don't dictate your diseases. Being at risk means that we need to piece together a customized plan that aims to lower those risks." - **CHRISTOPHER LEMAY, D.O.**

How Vicky Discovered the Root Cause of Her Migraines

Vicky is a TV producer, runs an NGO, and is a busy mom. But she's suffered from severe migraines since she was a teenager, and in 2019, after a three-week migraine, she knew she needed answers.

2019

2021

Her practitioner wanted to look at her DNA and the root cause of her migraines. They found that her stress would build up toxins her body couldn't get rid of. "For years, I was trying to manage my inflammation issue with hardcore medicine," Vicky says. But she wasn't mindful of her diet, which was "creating the perfect storm" for migraines. So she changed her diet. "These days, life is very different. I can actually feel the change."

PART 3
HOW
GENETICS
IMPACTS
OUR LIVES

Moving From Symptoms to Source

**Good health and wellness—and the
lack thereof—begins at the source.**

Imagine you're out
for a hike one day and find a beautiful
clearing next to a stream. It's a great place
for a picnic! But when you set out your picnic blanket,
you notice that there are empty bottles floating in the stream.
You pick the ones you see out so you can enjoy your picnic.
But soon, you see another empty bottle floating down the stream.
You pick it out—over and over again...

It's like plucking the next
empty bottle out of the stream.
The view may be fine for a while, but
eventually there will be another empty
bottle, or another symptom. It's
an unsustainable, tiring, and often
costly approach.

Unfortunately, this is a typical
approach in modern healthcare. When
patients come in with symptoms of a disease,
many practitioners simply treat the symptoms.

But what about finding the source of the issue? Tired of plucking bottles out of the stream all day, you decide to hike upstream to find the source of the issue. There it is! A broken recycling bin continues to drop bottles into water. Now that you know the source of the issue, you patch it up, and return to your beautiful picnic spot, finally unspoiled by floating trash.

Understanding a person's genes and lifestyle choices is like going to the source of the issue, and finding the root cause of why their body is functioning poorly. Once we know that, we're able to treat the root cause of our body's symptoms, rather than only masking the symptoms while allowing the underlying issues to go unchecked.

32

H=G+C Brings It All Together

Adding it all up to create a personalized health plan.

This downstream approach isn't helpful to those suffering from complex and chronic diseases, like diabetes, heart disease, and autoimmune disorders.

DOWNSTREAM

Not only do most health practitioners focus too much on treating symptoms instead of seeking out the underlying source of the dysfunction, but they also tend to give the same generalized treatment plans in their practice, failing to take individuality into account.

There is another, better way.
Health practitioners can deliver personalized treatment that can treat issues at the source by following this equation:
Health = Genetics + Choice

In order to increase HEALTH,
we need to increase our understanding of
GENETICS but also increase the right CHOICES
that optimize genetic expression for good.

The solution to a person's health, wellbeing,
and longevity isn't just solved by looking at their
genetics alone, or by looking at the lifestyle choices
they make. Instead, a person's HEALTH is made up
of both their GENETICS and their lifestyle CHOICES. Both
genetics and choices work together to create optimal—
or suboptimal—health.

CHOICE A

CHOICE B

Arina Finally Found Her Healthy Weight

Arina had gone on diets before, but couldn't lose weight. She sought out a genetic test and found that she didn't expend a lot of energy when she exercises, and exercise also caused inflammation—the root of the problem for her. "I found the test results enlightening. It makes me understand myself better," says Arina.

Now she hikes, and loves getting out in nature. She's also lost weight, is sleeping better, has more energy, and has less stress. Once she feared getting old because of the aches and pains. "Now I feel like I can get old—I wouldn't mind it!"

Why Do We Group Genes Together?

Pathways form the path forward towards better health.

Let's look at our equation again:
$$H = G + C$$
Does G just stand for one gene?
Would we look at just one genetic variation and use that to improve a patient's health?

Too often practitioners do that, and only look at one gene variation. But genes inherently work together to inform a number of biological processes. So why wouldn't we look at groups of genes together to gain better insights into our patients?

It's like being on a ship. You can try to hoist the sail with a single rope, but it won't be very strong! But if you braid two, three, or four ropes together, it'll be strong enough to hoist the sail and get you on your way.

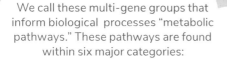

We call these multi-gene groups that inform biological processes "metabolic pathways." These pathways are found within six major categories:

1 CELLULAR

2 SYSTEMS

3 CARDIOVASCULAR

4 ENERGY

5 ACTIVITY

6 NUTRIENTS

Scientific Validity or Clinical Validity?

Which SNPs do we want to look at? That depends. Do they fit the following criteria:

What is their **Scientific Validity**, or is the science good enough?

What is their **Clinical Validity**, or how useful will this information be in helping me make a better clinical decision?

What Insights Can the Pathways Give Us?

Knowing the pathways means we can take action.

What insights can those six major pathway categories give us?

CELLULAR
Cells are the building blocks, but are they solid building blocks? This category uncovers how cells repair themselves, how prone they are to inflammation, oxidative stress, and more.

SYSTEMS
Are your higher-level systems keeping your body running? This category evaluates mood and behavior, brain health, hormone health, insulin balance, and other systems.

CARDIOVASCULAR
The cardiovascular system keeps our heart pumping and lungs filled, and this category tells us about blood pressure, cholesterol levels, clotting, and other functions.

ENERGY
What keeps our bodies energized? This category describes how an individual responds to calorie intake, their resistance to weight loss, how much energy they expend, and more.

ACTIVITY
Many people think they know the best exercise for them, but this category can tell you whether you're made for endurance or power exercise, your propensity for injury, and more.

NUTRIENTS
What nutrients we need to keep our bodies working optimally is informed by this category, which evaluates the effects of caffeine, choline, iron, gluten, and other nutrients.

The Story of Broccoli

Our bodies are continually exposed to toxins, from both outside sources in our environment as well as from inside our own bodies, so we always want to clear those toxins effectively to avoid unnecessary illness.

How can broccoli help?
Cruciferous vegetables produce a compound called sulforaphane —but we can't find it on its own.

When we eat vegetables like broccoli, and especially broccoli sprouts, the enzymes contained in them release and produce the super-detoxifier compound sulforaphane.

Why is sulforaphane so great?
Sulforaphane can switch on our detoxification genes as well as more than 500 genes that help protect our body.

What's the catch?
We need to eat the vegetables raw in order to create sulforaphane. Enjoy!

BROCCOLI

You may think that your ability to gain and lose weight is only determined by the foods you eat and the exercise you do. That's what most people think, because that's been the narrative for too long. Rarely does anyone talk about the important connection between your weight and how your genes interact with your diet and lifestyle. That's where DNA dieting comes in.

What Is a DNA Diet?

Genes can impact your nutrition; nutrition can impact your genes.

What is the scientific foundation of DNA dieting?

Genes impact an individual's hunger levels, eating behavior, and how full they feel.

Genes impact how someone's body will store those calories, and how they will burn them.

Genes impact inflammatory response which, if unchecked, can lead to weight gain or difficulty losing weight.

"Each client is so unique, it brings me great joy to show up and give them all the attention they need to feel supported, heard, and validated on their healing journey. I also love interpreting functional labs and designing personalized protocols. It takes the guesswork out of the treatment plan."

- RACHEL HEADINGS,
Virtual Functional Medicine Practitioner

Five Myths About Dieting and Your Genes

1

"Dieting is just about balancing energy in and energy out."

We've seen the equation of "energy in = energy out"—but science shows that this equation differs for each individual.

The question becomes: How do we understand what each person's equation looks like?

2

"People gain weight because they are greedy and have no self-control."

Genes impact not only how we burn calories, but also our taste, hunger, appetite, and satiety —two people will be impacted differently by eating the same large meal.

3

"Everyone can lose weight—just reduce calories and do more exercise."

Science has already proven that this isn't true, and that many people won't lose weight simply by reducing calories and exercising. So there must be another factor that can impact weight loss or gain.

"Children are overweight because of their parents."

④

Genetic research has shown that parents aren't always to blame. In a family that is fed the same food and that does the same exercise, you see siblings with very different body weight —meaning it's more complex than we think.

⑤

"There is one right diet."

There have been many diets called "the one": keto, paleo, low-carb... But the reality is that we all respond differently to the foods we eat, how much we eat, and the exercise we do.

FRESHLY SQUEEZED GRAPE JUICE
$15.00

Can Your DNA Give You Dieting Advice?

1

Your genes can give you insight into how you gain and lose weight, your appetite, hunger, fullness, eating habits, and more. Once you know, you can adjust meal timing, portions, plate proportions as well as addressing behaviors around eating.

6PM

UCP

Variations of this gene can result in a "sluggish metabolism."

FISH SNPs

2

Your genes can help you understand how you use and store different types of fats in your body, as well as your body's susceptibility to inflammation. Once you know, you can adjust fat intake and manage inflammation with diet and lifestyle changes.

3

Your genes can help you understand how well you burn calories that you've consumed and stored. Once you know, you can adjust your exercise and fitness approaches, or change the foods and the balance of nutrients you eat.

43

Genetics and Eating

What do I eat to stay healthy? High-carb, low-carb, plant-based, keto...? Well, what are your genes telling you? Genetic variations affect how we absorb and metabolize certain nutrients, enzymes, and fat. Some genes that affect fat stores include:

APOE
Variations tend to lead to higher triglyceride levels.

FTO
This gene influences obesity, and affects the "hunger hormone." It's also associated with Type 2 diabetes.

MC4R
This gene variation affects appetite control.

Genetics and Coffee

Do you take your coffee black, with cream and sugar, or not at all? First, doctors deemed coffee bad for your health. And then coffee became an important weapon to fight chronic disease. So which is it? It depends on your genes.

Meet the gene CYP1A2. Individuals with a variant of this gene will have slower caffeine processing ability than those who don't—and will experience the impacts of caffeine consumption, like anxiety, digestive issues, insomnia, and more. How would you like your coffee? Ask CYP1A2.

Genetics and Inflammation

Fatigue. Diabetes. Joint pain. Depression. Heart Disease. Cancer. What do they have in common? They're conditions caused by underlying inflammation. Is inflammation bad? Inflammation is actually needed by the body. It responds to infection, protects us, and is part of a healthy immune system—until it gets out of control. Toxins, stress, and even nutrients can cause severe inflammation that can lead to the issues above. But certain genes also determine inflammatory responses. Knowing how your genes respond to inflammation triggers can help you make choices that can turn the inflammation down.

The Story of Fatima

A pathway case study

Meet Fatima. She is 57 years old and the financial director of a clothing manufacturing business. She met with her practitioner due to a number of health concerns she was having, including:

severe fatigue

high stress and anxiety

a Parkinson's disease diagnosis

bloating and constipation

slow speech

high cholesterol

difficulty walking

Her work causes high stress and also exposure to toxins.

She's on antidepressants and L-Dopa for Parkinson's Disease, as well as other supplements.

meat-based curried stews

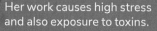
fried foods

pastries

HER DIET CONSISTS OF:

cakes

desserts

and fruit.

L-Dopa

FAMILY BACKGROUND

High blood pressure, cardiovascular disease, and dementia run in her family.

What do Fatima's genetic test and pathways tell us?

 CELLULAR PATHWAY
Fatima's ability to properly detoxify and repair DNA are impacted.

 SYSTEMS PATHWAY
Fatima's genes impact hormone balance, memory and brain health, mood and behavior, and bone health.

 CARDIOVASCULAR PATHWAY
Fatima's genes have a high impact in vascular health and cholesterol balance.

 ENERGY PATHWAY
Fatima's genes affect her appetite and satiety, and impact weight gain.

 ACTIVITY PATHWAY
Fatima's genes make her well suited for both endurance and power exercise.

  NUTRIENTS PATHWAY
Fatima's genes impact her levels of fatty acids, vitamin B12 transport, folate balance, and choline.

The solution? Fatima's practitioner's recommendations include:

INCREASING DETOXIFYING FOODS LIKE:

raw broccoli   cauliflower   leafy greens

wild-caught fish   and green tea

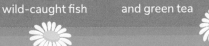

DECREASE INFLAMMATION

LOWERING HER TOXIN BURDEN AT WORK

NEW SUPPLEMENTS

AND OTHER RECOMMENDATIONS

PART 4
THE STORY OF
YOUR GENES

The Genetics Times

Extra! Extra! Read All About You

What can your genes tell you about your body?

From how your cells repair themselves to how bigger systems like your nervous system and cardiovascular system are working, your genetic results can tell you which nutrients are most needed for your unique body. They can also tell you which types of exercises may be optimal for your health and your performance goals.

What can your genes tell you about managing your weight?

Your genes can also give you insight into how easy or difficult it is to lose weight, and help you find weight management options that will be successful for how your unique body works.

What can your genes tell you about your optimal health?

Genes hold the blueprint to optimal health, and can show you how to build a solid foundation, where to put up walls, where to put windows and doors, and how to build a protective roof. Following the blueprint genes can provide means having an easy way to find personalized optimal health, wellness, and longevity.

What can your genes tell you about your susceptibility to certain diseases?

Certain genes can give us a lot of information on whether an individual is more susceptible to specific diseases—for example, BRCA genes predicting the likelihood of cancer.

Uncovering that information can help practitioners run more tests and create plans for prevention and care that can slow or even stop the progression of disease.

What can your genes tell you about your ancestry?

Your genes can help you understand where you came from and trace your lineage, but also what traits and disease susceptibilities have been passed down through your family.

What can your genes tell you about your fitness potential?

Exercise not working? It may be the wrong kind of exercise for your genes, which can tell you if your body responds better to either power exercises or endurance exercises. Create a better fitness plan with your genes.

What can your genes tell you about the right medications to take?

Imagine if pharmacological drug prescription wasn't trial and error, but that you knew which drugs would help—and which wouldn't? Your genes can also give you clues about how your body responds to different types of drugs, and if what you're taking now is beneficial to you. Genetics can help in mapping out more tailored treatment plans for managing chronic disease as well.

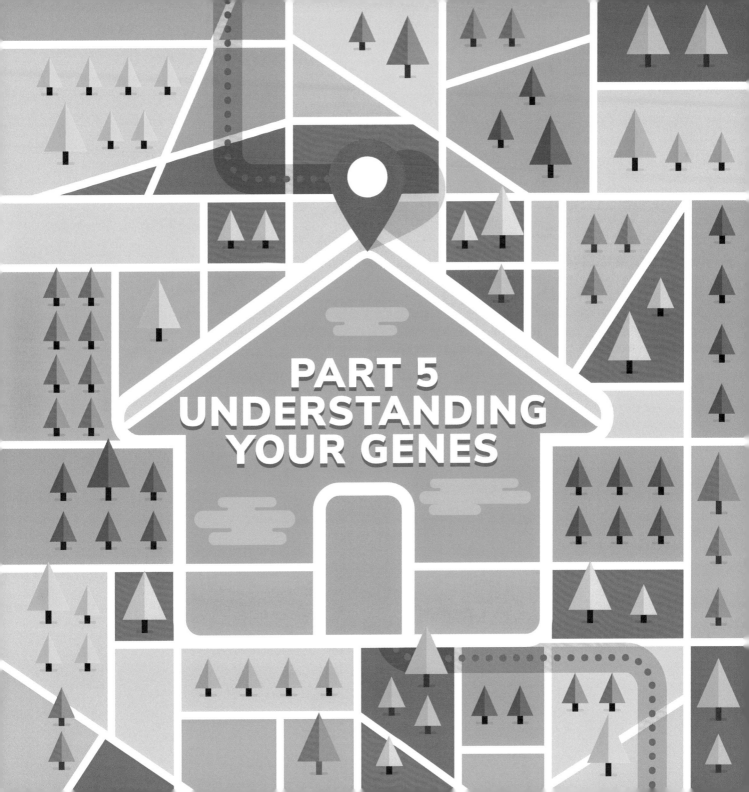

PART 5
UNDERSTANDING
YOUR GENES

How Can You Understand Your Genes?

Genetic testing and the insights it brings.

How do you get all these insights into who you are and how your body functions? Take a test!

Genetic testing is the opportunity to uncover your individual blueprint and discover the unique variations that influence how your genes express themselves. You'll also discover what choices you need to make in order to optimize your gene expression to live your best life.

FISH 'N SNPs

"Genetic testing is a great tool in functional medicine testing, and has helped several of my patients in managing their diseases. There are so many different SNPs that can help us to identify the underlying problem of my patients."

- ANSHUL GUPTA, Functional Medicine MD

What is Genetic Testing and How Does it Work?

Genetic testing is a fairly straightforward process: sample DNA is collected, tested, and analyzed, with a report generated from the findings.

1 Purchase and receive a genetic test kit right to your door.

2 A quick cheek swab will gather enough DNA needed. Send the test back.

3 A lab will test and map out the DNA.

4 The results will be analyzed, which can be translated into actionable recommendations.

OPTIMIZE METHYLATION

INCREASE VITAMIN D LEVELS

54

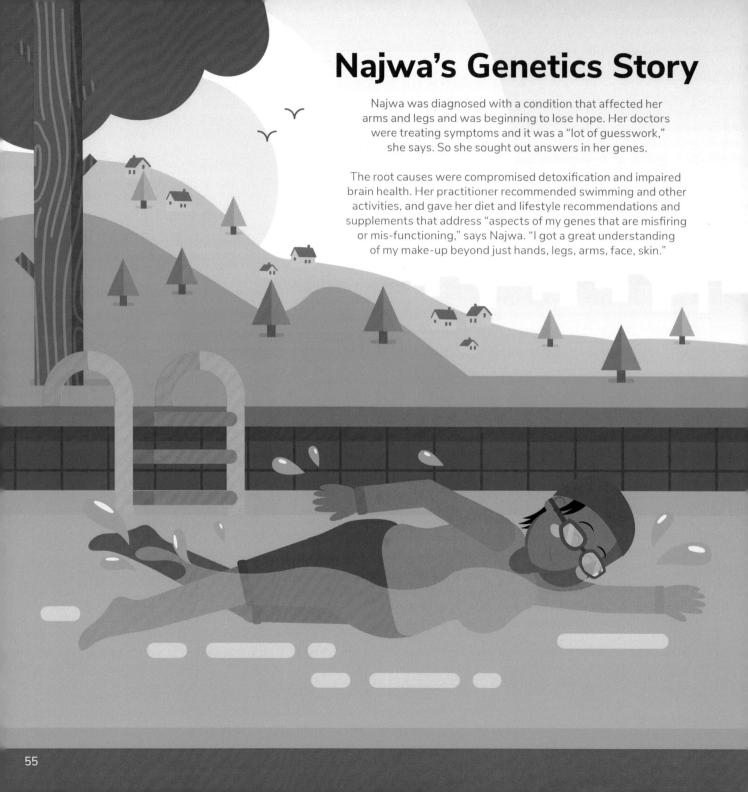

Najwa's Genetics Story

Najwa was diagnosed with a condition that affected her arms and legs and was beginning to lose hope. Her doctors were treating symptoms and it was a "lot of guesswork," she says. So she sought out answers in her genes.

The root causes were compromised detoxification and impaired brain health. Her practitioner recommended swimming and other activities, and gave her diet and lifestyle recommendations and supplements that address "aspects of my genes that are misfiring or mis-functioning," says Najwa. "I got a great understanding of my make-up beyond just hands, legs, arms, face, skin."

What Are the Different Types of Genetic Tests?

There are different types of genetic tests available. They include:

 Diagnostic tests
These tests are used to diagnose medical conditions.

 Carrier tests
These tests find if someone carries a particular condition.

 Pharmacogenetic tests
These tests can anticipate someone's response to drugs or therapy (like chemotherapy).

 Nutrigenetic tests
These tests give insight into responses to nutrients.

 Ancestry tests
These tests show how someone is related to an ancestral group.

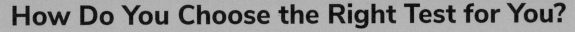

How Do You Choose the Right Test for You?

Which test you want to use depends on the goals you want to achieve, which can include:

 Wanting to learn more about your health and wellness

 Wanting to understand your full exercise potential

 Wanting to understand how you gain and lose weight

 Wanting to learn more about a genetic disposition that runs in your family

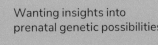 Wanting insights into prenatal genetic possibilities

10 Reasons to Test your Genes

What you can learn from your genetic code.

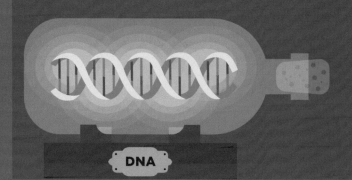

DNA

How to Lose Weight

Weight loss is about more than eating fewer calories. Your genetics can tell you where appetite, satiety, eating behavior, and more is standing in your way.

Avoiding Injuries

Your genes can help you understand your genetically-determined susceptibility to certain injuries, which can help you mitigate risk during exercise.

Natural Detox Power

Toxic compounds are all around us—how quickly and effectively does your body process and eliminate these harmful hazards?

Inflammation Control

Chronic disease and unchecked inflammation are linked, and gaining insight into your inflammation genes can help reverse or prevent illness.

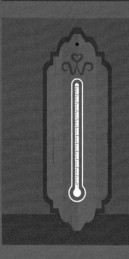

Vitamin D Production

Vitamin D3 controls the expression of over 1000 genes, yet most of us don't have enough of it. Testing your genes can assess your metabolism of Vitamin D.

Metabolism Response

Certain genes influence metabolism, and determine your response to different types of fat, as well as protein, carbohydrates, and more.

Coffee Intake

A genetic test can tell you how fast your body metabolizes caffeine, which can help you optimize or limit your coffee intake.

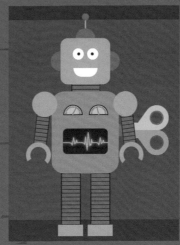

Energy Levels

B12 and folate affect our energy and are controlled by certain genes. Learn more about those genes and you can make better choices to boost your energy.

The Best Exercises

Forget what others tell you is the best exercise for you— your genes can give you insight into your fitness, performance, recovery, and more.

WAKE UP & WORK OUT

Daily Health Choices

Knowing more about your genes can point you towards simple changes you can make in your diet and lifestyle that can have a big impact.

Your Health Journey

Where are you journeying to on your health path?

1

Starting the Journey

You know your health needs to change. But where do you start? Each unique person walks their own health path. In order to find the path tailored specifically for you, the journey begins by understanding your genetic code.

2

Pathway Analysis

Genetic testing provides one piece of the health puzzle. Diet and lifestyle choices, family and medical history, and many other factors all play an equally important role in human health. Practitioners and qualified coaches can help you bring all the pieces together and co-create a realistic, personal plan with you!

3

Diet and Lifestyle Changes

Here is where the change happens. As you begin to understand how your genes impact your cells, your systems, and the food you eat, you can begin to make changes to your diet and lifestyle that better align with who you are.

5

Targeted Supplements

Now that you better understand the way your genes work and how they impact your bodily systems, you can choose the right supplements to optimize those pathways.

4

Precision Functional Testing

Knowing more about how your unique body functions means that your practitioner can be more personalized in their care for you. This can include more precise functional and blood testing that can get to the root of your maladies.

The Story of Gordon

A pathway case study

Meet Gordon. He is 28 years old and is a diver on an oil rig. He met with his practitioner because he wanted insights into better fitness training and performance:

He's training for his first Iron Man

He used to be a long-distance swimmer, but now gets tired easily

He's prone to colds and flus

He has recurring joint pain

He struggles with low mood and depression

He has a healthy diet, and recently went vegan. He also drinks protein shakes and sports supplements.

He trains twice a day, and runs, cycles, swims, and lifts weights.

His work is stressful, exposes him to toxins, and has him switching between day and night shifts.

FAMILY BACKGROUND   His family is active, yet there's a history of depression, anxiety, and cardiovascular disease.

What do Gordon's genetic test and pathways tell us?

 CELLULAR PATHWAY
Gordon has a slower methylation capacity, which impacts neurochemical imbalances, reduced detoxification, and hormone dysregulation.

 SYSTEMS PATHWAY
Gordon's genes impact his mood and behavior, memory and brain health, hormone balance, and collagen, which can result in joint injury.

 ENERGY PATHWAY
Gordon's genes show a low genetic potential for weight gain and energy imbalance.

 ACTIVITY PATHWAY
Gordon's genes show great athletic capability, high training response, and endurance exercise potential.

 NUTRIENTS PATHWAY
Gordon's genes impact his ability to metabolize caffeine, as well as vitamin B12 and folate.

The solution? Gordon's practitioner's recommendations include:

INCREASING DETOXIFYING FOODS LIKE:

cruciferous vegetables

asparagus

apples

and quality proteins

GETTING MORE
SLEEP IN A DARK ROOM

ADJUSTING HIS EXERCISE
TO PREVENT STRESS
AND INJURY

DECREASING TOXIN
EXPOSURE AT WORK

NEW SUPPLEMENTS

AND OTHER
RECOMMENDATIONS

PART 6
TAKING
CONTROL OF
YOUR HEALTH

From DNA Data to Daily Decisions

How can your genes help you live a better life?

With your personal blueprint and all these new valuable insights about yourself, you can take action forward towards a better, happier, and healthier life.

The power of your genetics is in your hands, and in the daily, DNA-driven decisions you make.

How to Use Your Genes to Make Diet Decisions

Knowing how your body responds to certain foods can help you make better, more personalized food choices that are guided by your own genes.

How to Use Your Genes to Make Lifestyle Decisions

How can I improve my sleep? Reduce my stress? Avoid certain harmful environments? Your genes can help you determine which lifestyle choices are best for you.

How to Use Your Genes to Make Targeted Supplement Decisions

Knowing the possible impact of your genes can point the way towards specific supplements that will be the most beneficial for you.

How to Use Your Genes to Make Exercise Decisions

Do your genes tell you that your body would be healthier doing more endurance-based exercises? Adjust your fitness for optimized health.

FISH N SNPs

ENJOY YOUR JOURNEY
TO BEING AS HEALTHY
AS YOU CAN BE!

Yael Joffe

PhD
Founder & CSO 3X4 Genetics

Our personal North Star is not out there in space, but rather right here inside each of us.

Over the past year I have been lucky enough to interview some of the most inspiring practitioners and thought leaders who are boldly changing the way nutrition and medicine are being taught and practiced around the world.

Profound knowledge and insight has come to me in these conversations. Dr. Dale Bredesen, The New York Times best-selling author of *The End of Alzheimer's* spoke about a time when "Alzheimer's will be optional." I can't get those words out of my head. Imagine! Right now it is widely accepted that nothing can be done to prevent or delay the onset of Alzheimer's disease, but Dr. Bredesen's hopeful message is that this is not true and that much can be done!

Everything we do in our lives links in some way to what we have inherited; our genes affect so much about us—from our eating and exercise behavior, to how little we sleep, and how we respond to stress.

Today, and even more so in the future, genetics will enable and empower each of us to make the best possible decisions for ourselves and our bodies every minute of every day, throughout our lives. Our genes are our own personal North Star, guiding us through the different stages, phases, peaks, and troughs of our journey.

I was reminded of the power of genetics by Dr. Jeff Bland when he spoke with me about how genes allow us to explore the potential greatness within every human being. That the goodness of genes can free us from all bias. This is where art meets science.

The potential of genetics is so much more than just data, it should never be analyzed or considered alone. To achieve true personalization we need to ensure that alongside our genes we integrate multiple data streams, as Dr. Gottfried mentioned in her foreword for this book, and we also need to ensure that alongside our genes we address other aspects of our being such as social connection, community support, trauma, stress, and finding purpose in our lives.

This beautiful book is the book I would have wanted and so appreciated when I first heard about the exciting new field of nutrigenomics back in 2000. I hope these pages give you everything you need to dip your toes into the exhilarating world of genetics and to start your own exploration journey of deep personal insight.

My wish for you is that you find some of the answers and inspiration you have been looking for, just like I did! Welcome to the world of genetics.